KT-571-129

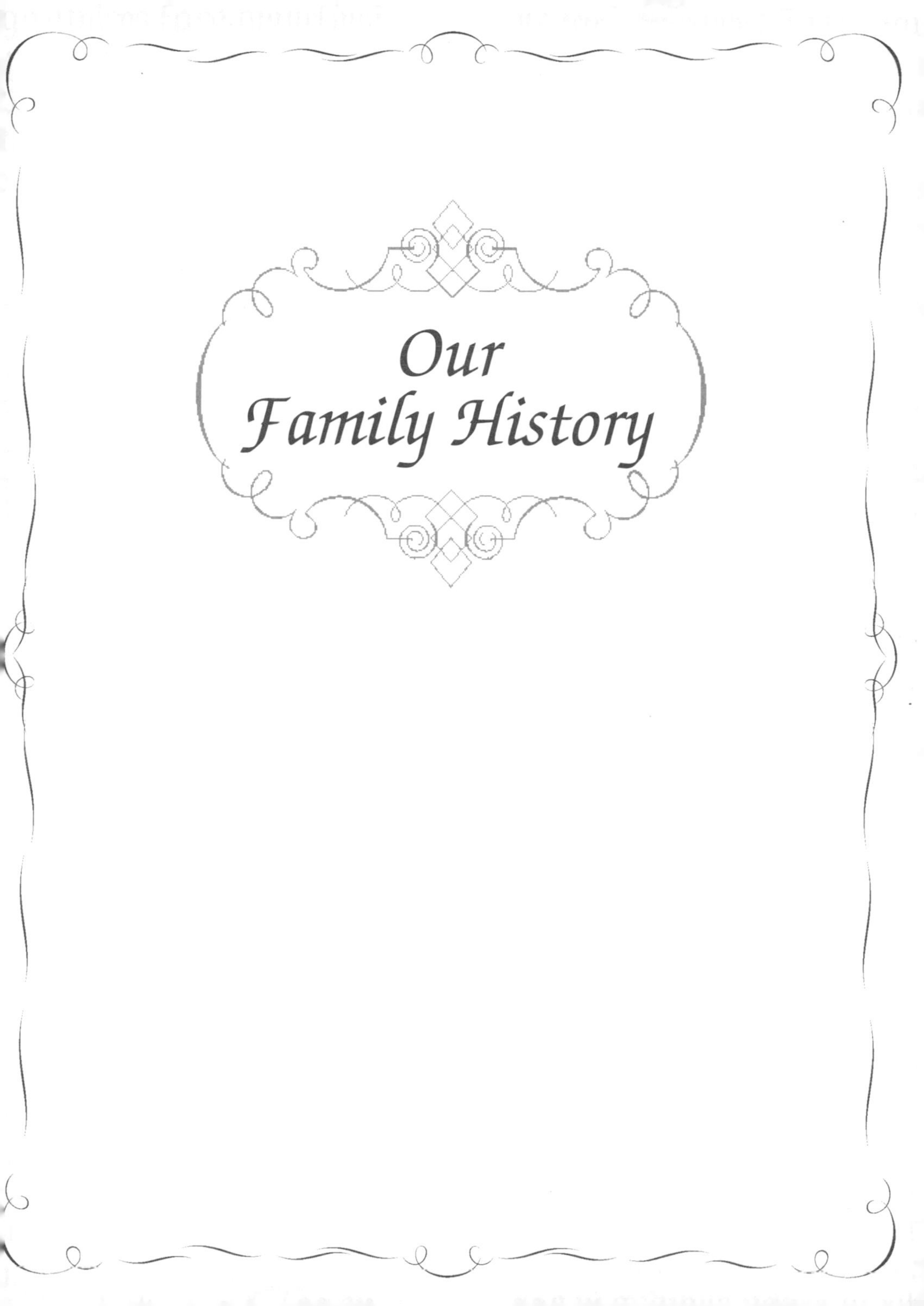

Our Family History

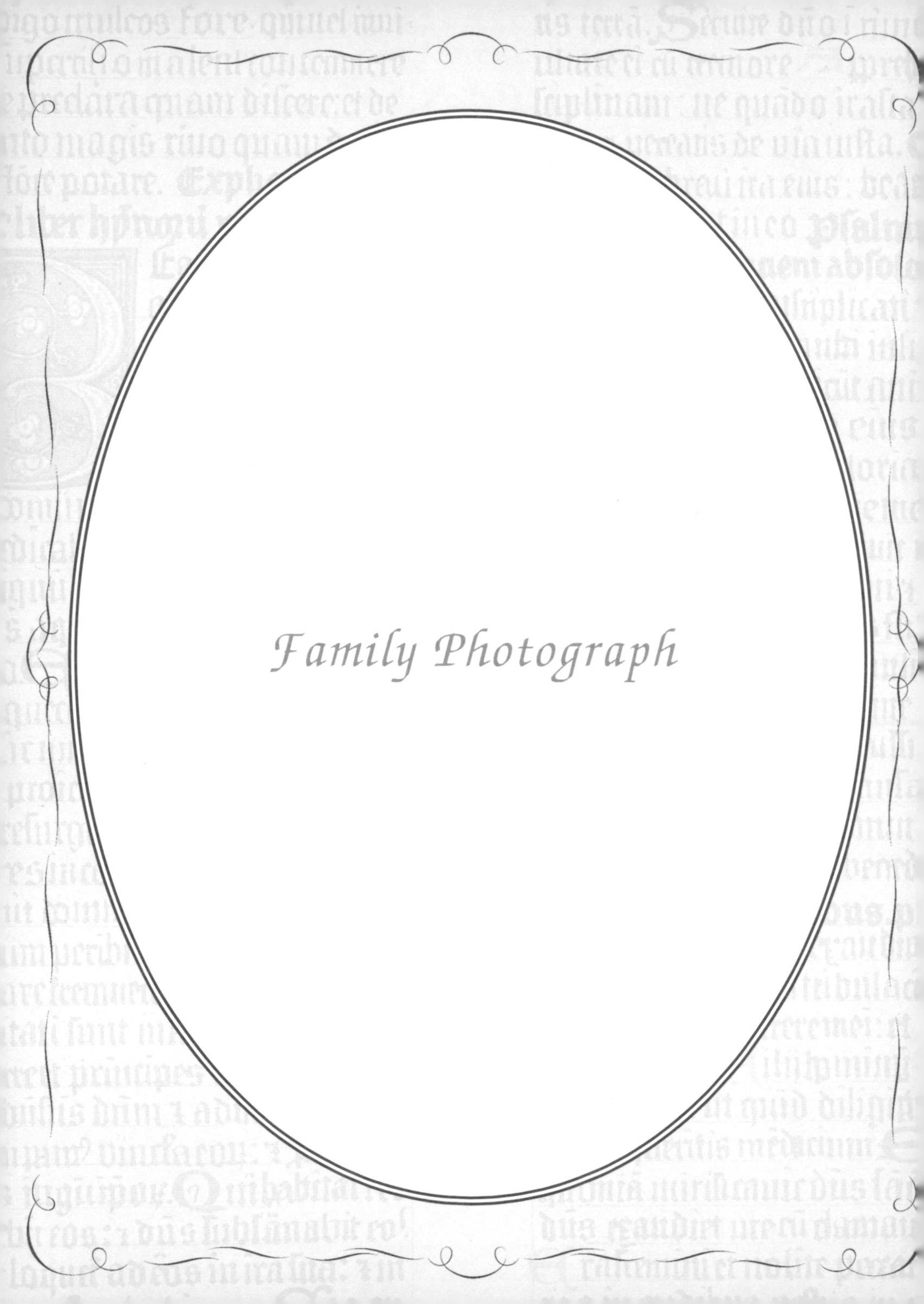
Family Photograph

Our
Family History

4 North Parade

Bath BA1 1LF

Printed in Hong Kong

CONTENTS

with quotations and woodcuts throughout,
and pages for Notes and Photographs

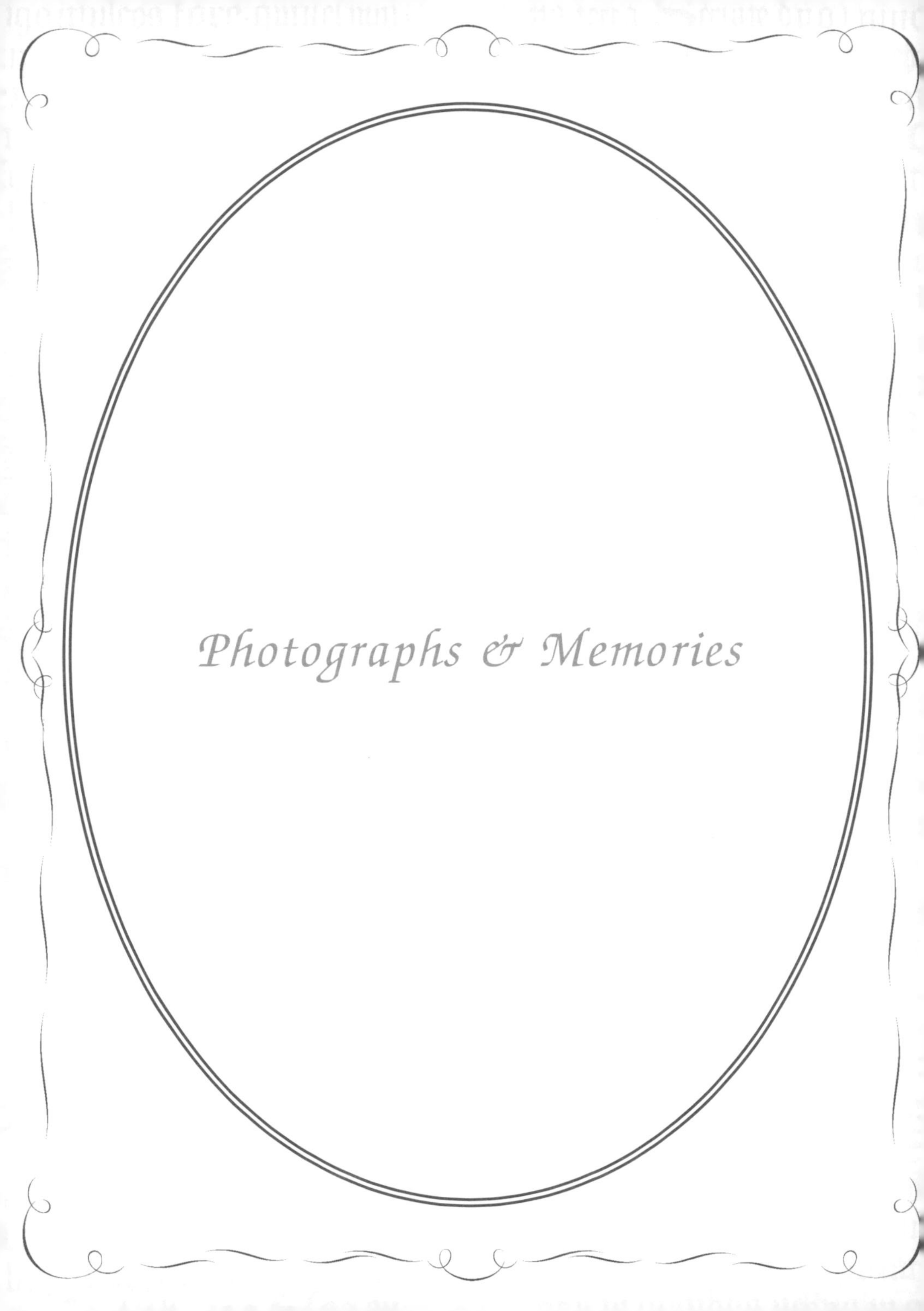
Photographs & Memories

OUR FAMILY HISTORY

Have you ever thought about who your ancestors were? – what they did, what they achieved, where they came from? Well, if so, this book is for you. Designed to keep forever a record of your family history, it also gives valuable information and useful hints as to how to go about your research.

From the youngest child just born to your great great grandparents, this book gives you a unique opportunity to learn more about the origin of your direct descendants. More than anything, this is a book about people, not just names, dates and places.

We sincerely hope that you enjoy compiling your family history. When complete, it will provide a treasure-trove of information, achievements and memories, and will be an wonderful gift for your children and grandchildren And maybe you can even learn more about yourself from studying your ancestors. For as Walt Whitman once wrote:

"The Past! the dark unfathom'd retrospect!
The teeming gulf! the sleepers and the shadows!
The past! the infinite greatness of the past!
for what is the present after all,
but a growth out of the past?"

Tracing your family history

Here are some useful hints to help you trace your family tree.

1. LIVING RELATIVES

First-hand information is always the best. Your elderly relatives should be able to give you much information about their own families, their parents and grandparents, where they lived, what jobs they did and so on. Make a list of as many names as possible. They may have hoarded old documents, certificates and family photographs which will help you in your investigation.

2. OFFICIAL RECORDS

General Register Office

The General Register Office, located in St Catherine's House, Kingsway, London WC2B 6JP holds records dating back to 1st July 1837 for England and Wales. There is no charge for searching the indexes.

You can request a copy of your own birth certificate, and from this you can work backwards, looking for both your parents' birth and marriage certificates, the marriage certificates of both sets of grandparents and so on. Once the entry has been found a full certificate can be supplied for a small fee.

Scottish Record Office

If you were born in Scotland you will need to consult the Scottish Record Office (PO Box 36, HM General Register House, Edinburgh EH1 3YY).

Local Parish Registers

For records of births, marriages and deaths before 1837 you will need to consult local parish registers which were first ordered to be kept in 1538. Not all parish registers have survived and many did not begin until the late 1600's. Most registers existing are in the hands of the clergy or locked for safe-keeping in the County or Diocesan Record Offices. Consulting these can be a lengthy process, especially in the larger cities, or if your families moved around the country a lot. However, there are some short-cuts. Phillimore and Co Ltd (Shopwyke Hall, Chichester, West Sussex PO20 6BQ) have published hundreds of parish registers thus minimizing the necessity for travelling all over the country. The Society of Genealogists (37 Harrington Gardens, London SW7 4JX) also hold many copies.

To trace your ancestors you will thus need to know which parish they were born in. You can search for this in the census returns.

3. CENSUS

A census has been taken every 10 years from 1801 and returns for 1841, 1851 and 1861 are housed in the Public Records Office (Land Registry Building, Portugal Street, London WC2A 1LR) and can be inspected by the general public. The census return gives information as to where each person was born, indicating which parish registers should be targeted for your searches.

4. OTHER DENOMINATIONS

Parish registers did not cover Dissentors, Foreigners and Jews. Sources for these groups can be found in the 12 volume National Index of Parish Registers published by Phillimore & Co. The Index includes records for the following groups: Nonconformists, Presbyterians, Independents, Baptists, Society of Friends, Moravians, Methodists, Foreign Churches, Roman Catholics and for Jewish Genealogy.

We wish you every success in your endeavour to trace your ancestors.

"To be able to enjoy one's past life
is to live twice."

MARTIAL

Our Family History

"To forget one's ancestors is to be a brook without a source, a tree without a root."

CHINESE PROVERB

A history of the .... family

The Marriage

....

and

....

were joined together in marriage on

....

at

....

Husband's Genealogy

Husband's Full Name _______________

Birth Date _______________

Birth Place _______________

Father's Full Name _______________

Mother's Full Name _______________

Brothers & Sisters

"An ideal wife is any woman who has an ideal husband."

BOOTH TARKINGTON

Wife's Genealogy

Wife's Full Name _._

Birth Date _._

Birth Place _._

Father's Full Name _._

Mother's Full Name _._

Brothers & Sisters

Family Notes

Family Notes

Family Notes

Family Notes

Our Children

Full Name _______________

____

Date of Birth _______________

Place of Birth _______________

Weight _______________

Our Children

Full Name ____________________________________

____

Date of Birth ____________________________________

Place of Birth ____________________________________

Weight ____________________________________

"Children are the true connoisseurs.
What's precious to them has no price, only value."

BEL KAUFMAN

Our Children

Full Name _______________

____

Date of Birth _______________

Place of Birth _______________

Weight _______________

Our Children

åFull Name ______________________________

____

Date of Birth ______________________________

Place of Birth ______________________________

Weight ______________________________

Our Children

Full Name ___________________

____

Date of Birth ___________________

Place of Birth ___________________

Weight ___________________

Our Children

Full Name

Date of Birth

Place of Birth

Weight

Our Grandchildren

Full Name ______________________

____

Date of Birth ______________________

Place of Birth ______________________

Weight ______________________

Our Grandchildren

Full Name

Date of Birth

Place of Birth

Weight

Our Grandchildren

Full Name ______________________

____

Date of Birth ______________________

Place of Birth ______________________

Weight ______________________

Our Grandchildren

Full Name _______________

____

Date of Birth _______________

Place of Birth _______________

Weight _______________

Our Grandchildren

Full Name ______________________

____

Date of Birth ______________________

Place of Birth ______________________

Weight ______________________

Our Grandchildren

Full Name ______________________

____

Date of Birth ______________________

Place of Birth ______________________

Weight ______________________

Our Grandchildren

Full Name ______________________________

____

Date of Birth ______________________________

Place of Birth ______________________________

Weight ______________________________

Our Grandchildren

Full Name _______________________

____

Date of Birth _______________________

Place of Birth _______________________

Weight _______________________

Our Great Grandchildren

Full Name

Date of Birth

Place of Birth

Weight

Our Great Grandchildren

Full Name _

_ _ _ _ _ _ _ _ _ _ _ _ _ _ _ _ _ _ _ _

Date of Birth _

Place of Birth _

Weight _

"In a brief space the generations of beings are changed, and, like runners, pass on the torches of life."

Lucretius

Family Notes

Family Notes

Family Notes

Family Notes

Our Family Tree

Our Children

Our Grand-Children

Spouse

Spouse

usband

Spouse

Wife

Spouse

Spouse

Spouse

Parents

Husband's Father

Date of Marriage

Other Children

Husband

Husband's Mother

Date of Marriage

Wife's Father

Wife

Date of Marriage

Other Children

Wife's Mother

Our Ancestors

Grandparents

Husband's Paternal Grandfather's Name

Husband's Paternal Grandmother's Name

Husband's Maternal Grandfather's Name

Husband's Maternal Grandmother's Name

Wife's Paternal Grandfather's Name

Wife's Paternal Grandmother's Name

Wife's Maternal Grandfather's Name

Wife's Maternal Grandmother's Name

Great Grandparents

Husband's Great Grandfather's Name

Husband's Great Grandmother's Name

Husband's Great Grandfather's Name

Husband's Great Grandmother's Name

Husband's Great Grandfather's Name

Husband's Great Grandmother's Name

Husband's Great Grandfather's Name

Husband's Great Grandmother's Name

Wife's Great Grandfather's Name

Wife's Great Grandmother's Name

Wife's Great Grandfather's Name

Wife's Great Grandmother's Name

Wife's Great Grandfather's Name

Wife's Great Grandmother's Name

Wife's Great Grandfather's Name

Wife's Great Grandmother's Name

Husband's Ancestral Chart

Father's Name

Date of Birth Died

Place of Birth

Notes

Husband

Mother's Name

Date of Birth Died

Place of Birth

Notes

"A people without history is like wind on the buffalo grass."
SIOUX PROVERB

Great Grandfather's Name

Grandfather's Name

Date of Birth Died

Place of Birth

Great Grandmother's Name

Great Grandfather's Name

Grandmother's Name

Date of Birth Died

Place of Birth

Great Grandmother's Name

Great Grandfather's Name

Grandfather's Name

Date of Birth Died

Place of Birth

Great Grandmother's Name

Great Grandfather's Name

Grandmother's Name

Date of Birth Died

Place of Birth

Great Grandmother's Name

Great Great Grandfather's Name

Great Great Grandmother's Name

Great Great Grandfather's Name

Great Great Grandmother's Name

Great Great Grandfather's Name

Great Great Grandmother's Name

Great Great Grandfather's Name

Great Great Grandmother's Name

Great Great Grandfather's Name

Great Great Grandmother's Name

Great Great Grandfather's Name

Great Great Grandmother's Name

Great Great Grandfather's Name

Great Great Grandmother's Name

Great Great Grandfather's Name

Great Great Grandmother's Name

Great Great Grandparents

Great Great Great Grandparents

Family Notes

Husband's Family

Brothers & Sisters

Born *Died*

Spouse

Born *Died*

Spouse

Born *Died*

Spouse

Born *Died*

Spouse

Born *Died*

Spouse

Nephews & Nieces

Born Died Spouse
Born Died Spouse
Born Died Spouse
Born Died Spouse
Born Died Spouse

Born Died Spouse
Born Died Spouse
Born Died Spouse
Born Died Spouse
Born Died Spouse

Born Died Spouse
Born Died Spouse
Born Died Spouse
Born Died Spouse
Born Died Spouse

Born Died Spouse
Born Died Spouse
Born Died Spouse
Born Died Spouse
Born Died Spouse

Born Died Spouse
Born Died Spouse
Born Died Spouse
Born Died Spouse
Born Died Spouse

Husband's Father's Family

Husband's Father's Brothers and Sisters

Born Died

Spouse

Born Died

Spouse

Born Died

Spouse

Born Died

Spouse

Born Died

Spouse

Husband's Father's Nephews & Nieces

Born	Died	Spouse
Born	Died	Spouse
Born	Died	Spouse
Born	Died	Spouse
Born	Died	Spouse

Born	Died	Spouse
Born	Died	Spouse
Born	Died	Spouse
Born	Died	Spouse
Born	Died	Spouse

Born	Died	Spouse
Born	Died	Spouse
Born	Died	Spouse
Born	Died	Spouse
Born	Died	Spouse

Born	Died	Spouse
Born	Died	Spouse
Born	Died	Spouse
Born	Died	Spouse
Born	Died	Spouse

Born	Died	Spouse
Born	Died	Spouse
Born	Died	Spouse
Born	Died	Spouse
Born	Died	Spouse

Husband's Mother's Family

Husband's Mother's Brothers & Sisters

Born Died

Spouse

Born Died

Spouse

Born Died

Spouse

Born Died

Spouse

Born Died

Spouse

Husband's Mother's Nephews & Nieces

Born	Died	Spouse
Born	Died	Spouse
Born	Died	Spouse
Born	Died	Spouse
Born	Died	Spouse

Born	Died	Spouse
Born	Died	Spouse
Born	Died	Spouse
Born	Died	Spouse
Born	Died	Spouse

Born	Died	Spouse
Born	Died	Spouse
Born	Died	Spouse
Born	Died	Spouse
Born	Died	Spouse

Born	Died	Spouse
Born	Died	Spouse
Born	Died	Spouse
Born	Died	Spouse
Born	Died	Spouse

Born	Died	Spouse
Born	Died	Spouse
Born	Died	Spouse
Born	Died	Spouse
Born	Died	Spouse

Husband's Paternal Grandparents

Grandfather

Husband's Grandfather's Brothers & Sisters

Born Died

Spouse

Born Died

Spouse

Born Died

Spouse

Born Died

Spouse

Born Died

Spouse

Husband's Grandfather's Nephews & Nieces

Born	Died	Spouse
Born	Died	Spouse
Born	Died	Spouse
Born	Died	Spouse
Born	Died	Spouse

Born	Died	Spouse
Born	Died	Spouse
Born	Died	Spouse
Born	Died	Spouse
Born	Died	Spouse

Born	Died	Spouse
Born	Died	Spouse
Born	Died	Spouse
Born	Died	Spouse
Born	Died	Spouse

Born	Died	Spouse
Born	Died	Spouse
Born	Died	Spouse
Born	Died	Spouse
Born	Died	Spouse

Born	Died	Spouse
Born	Died	Spouse
Born	Died	Spouse
Born	Died	Spouse
Born	Died	Spouse

Husband's Paternal Grandparents

Grandmother

Husband's Grandmother's Brothers & Sisters

Born Died

Spouse

Born Died

Spouse

Born Died

Spouse

Born Died

Spouse

Born Died

Spouse

Husband's Grandmother's Nephews & Nieces

Born ______ *Died* ______ *Spouse* ______
Born ______ *Died* ______ *Spouse* ______
Born ______ *Died* ______ *Spouse* ______
Born ______ *Died* ______ *Spouse* ______
Born ______ *Died* ______ *Spouse* ______

Born *Died* *Spouse*
Born ______ *Died* ______ *Spouse* ______
Born ______ *Died* ______ *Spouse* ______
Born ______ *Died* ______ *Spouse* ______
Born ______ *Died* ______ *Spouse* ______

Born ______ *Died* ______ *Spouse* ______
Born ______ *Died* ______ *Spouse* ______
Born ______ *Died* ______ *Spouse* ______
Born ______ *Died* ______ *Spouse* ______
Born ______ *Died* ______ *Spouse* ______

Born ______ *Died* ______ *Spouse* ______
Born ______ *Died* ______ *Spouse* ______
Born ______ *Died* ______ *Spouse* ______
Born ______ *Died* ______ *Spouse* ______
Born ______ *Died* ______ *Spouse* ______

Born ______ *Died* ______ *Spouse* ______
Born ______ *Died* ______ *Spouse* ______
Born ______ *Died* ______ *Spouse* ______
Born ______ *Died* ______ *Spouse* ______
Born ______ *Died* ______ *Spouse* ______

Husband's Maternal Grandparents

Grandfather

Husband's Grandfather's Brothers & Sisters

Born Died

Spouse

Born Died

Spouse

Born Died

Spouse

Born Died

Spouse

Born Died

Spouse

Husband's Grandfather's Nephews & Nieces

Born Died Spouse
Born Died Spouse
Born Died Spouse
Born Died Spouse
Born Died Spouse

Born Died Spouse
Born Died Spouse
Born Died Spouse
Born Died Spouse
Born Died Spouse

Born Died Spouse
Born Died Spouse
Born Died Spouse
Born Died Spouse
Born Died Spouse

Born Died Spouse
Born Died Spouse
Born Died Spouse
Born Died Spouse
Born Died Spouse

Born Died Spouse
Born Died Spouse
Born Died Spouse
Born Died Spouse
Born Died Spouse

Husband's Maternal Grandparents

Grandmother

Husband's Grandmother's Brothers & Sisters

Born Died

Spouse

Born Died

Spouse

Born Died

Spouse

Born Died

Spouse

Born Died

Spouse

Husband's Grandmother's Nephews & Nieces

Born Died Spouse
Born Died Spouse
Born Died Spouse
Born Died Spouse
Born Died Spouse

Born Died Spouse
Born Died Spouse
Born Died Spouse
Born Died Spouse
Born Died Spouse

Born Died Spouse
Born Died Spouse
Born Died Spouse
Born Died Spouse
Born Died Spouse

Born Died Spouse
Born Died Spouse
Born Died Spouse
Born Died Spouse
Born Died Spouse

Born Died Spouse
Born Died Spouse
Born Died Spouse
Born Died Spouse
Born Died Spouse

Husband's Great Grandparents

Husband's Great Grandparents

Family Notes

Family Notes

Family Notes

Family Notes

Wife's Ancestral Chart

Father's Name

Date of Birth Died

Place of Birth

Notes

Wife

Mother's Name

Date of Birth Died

Place of Birth

Notes

"Remember me when
I am gone away,
Gone far away into the silent land."
CHRISTINA ROSSETTI

Great Grandfather's Name

Grandfather's Name

Date of Birth

Great Grandfather's Name

Grandmother's Name

Date of Birth *Died*

Place of Birth

Great Grandmother's Name

Great Grandfather's Name

Grandfather's Name

Date of Birth *Died*

Place of Birth

Great Grandmother's Name

Great Grandfather's Name

Grandmother's Name

Date of Birth *Died*

Place of Birth

Great Grandmother's Name

Great Great Grandfather's Name

Great Great Grandmother's Name

Great Great Grandfather's Name

Great Great Grandmother's Name

Great Great Grandfather's Name

Great Great Grandmother's Name

Great Great Grandfather's Name

Great Great Grandmother's Name

Great Great Grandfather's Name

Great Great Grandmother's Name

Great Great Grandfather's Name

Great Great Grandmother's Name

Great Great Grandfather's Name

Great Great Grandmother's Name

Great Great Grandfather's Name

Great Great Grandmother's Name

Great Great Grandparents

Great Great Great Grandparents

Family Notes

Wife's Family

Brothers & Sisters

Born Died

Spouse

Born Died

Spouse

Born Died

Spouse

Born Died

Spouse

Born Died

Spouse

Nephews & Nieces

Born Died Spouse
Born Died Spouse
Born Died Spouse
Born Died Spouse
Born Died Spouse

Born Died Spouse
Born Died Spouse
Born Died Spouse
Born Died Spouse
Born Died Spouse

Born Died Spouse
Born Died Spouse
Born Died Spouse
Born Died Spouse
Born Died Spouse

Born Died Spouse
Born Died Spouse
Born Died Spouse
Born Died Spouse
Born Died Spouse

Born Died Spouse
Born Died Spouse
Born Died Spouse
Born Died Spouse
Born Died Spouse

Wife's Father's Family

Wife's Father's Brothers & Sisters

Born *Died*

Spouse

Born *Died*

Spouse

Born *Died*

Spouse

Born *Died*

Spouse

Born *Died*

Spouse

Wife's Father's Nephews & Nieces

Born	Died	Spouse
Born	Died	Spouse
Born	Died	Spouse
Born	Died	Spouse
Born	Died	Spouse

Born	Died	Spouse
Born	Died	Spouse
Born	Died	Spouse
Born	Died	Spouse
Born	Died	Spouse

Born	Died	Spouse
Born	Died	Spouse
Born	Died	Spouse
Born	Died	Spouse
Born	Died	Spouse

Born	Died	Spouse
Born	Died	Spouse
Born	Died	Spouse
Born	Died	Spouse
Born	Died	Spouse

Born	Died	Spouse
Born	Died	Spouse
Born	Died	Spouse
Born	Died	Spouse
Born	Died	Spouse

Wife's Mother's Family

Brothers & Sisters

Born Died

Spouse

Born Died

Spouse

Born Died

Spouse

Born Died

Spouse

Born Died

Spouse

Nephews & Nieces

Born Died Spouse
Born Died Spouse
Born Died Spouse
Born Died Spouse
Born Died Spouse

Born Died Spouse
Born Died Spouse
Born Died Spouse
Born Died Spouse
Born Died Spouse

Born Died Spouse
Born Died Spouse
Born Died Spouse
Born Died Spouse
Born Died Spouse

Born Died Spouse
Born Died Spouse
Born Died Spouse
Born Died Spouse
Born Died Spouse

Born Died Spouse
Born Died Spouse
Born Died Spouse
Born Died Spouse
Born Died Spouse

Wife's Paternal Grandparents

Grandfather

Wife's Grandfather's Brothers & Sisters

Born *Died*

Spouse

Born *Died*

Spouse

Born *Died*

Spouse

Born *Died*

Spouse

Born *Died*

Spouse

Wife's Grandfather's Nephews & Nieces

Born Died Spouse
Born Died Spouse
Born Died Spouse
Born Died Spouse
Born Died Spouse

Born Died Spouse
Born Died Spouse
Born Died Spouse
Born Died Spouse
Born Died Spouse

Born Died Spouse
Born Died Spouse
Born Died Spouse
Born Died Spouse
Born Died Spouse

Born Died Spouse
Born Died Spouse
Born Died Spouse
Born Died Spouse
Born Died Spouse

Born Died Spouse
Born Died Spouse
Born Died Spouse
Born Died Spouse
Born Died Spouse

Wife's Paternal Grandparents

Grandmother

Wife's Grandmother's Brothers & Sisters

Born Died

Spouse

Born Died

Spouse

Born Died

Spouse

Born Died

Spouse

Born Died

Spouse

Wife's Grandmother's Nephews & Nieces

Born Died Spouse
Born Died Spouse
Born Died Spouse
Born Died Spouse
Born Died Spouse

Born Died Spouse
Born Died Spouse
Born Died Spouse
Born Died Spouse
Born Died Spouse

Born Died Spouse
Born Died Spouse
Born Died Spouse
Born Died Spouse
Born Died Spouse

Born Died Spouse
Born Died Spouse
Born Died Spouse
Born Died Spouse
Born Died Spouse

Born Died Spouse
Born Died Spouse
Born Died Spouse
Born Died Spouse
Born Died Spouse

Wife's Maternal Grandparents

Grandfather

Wife's Grandfather's Brothers & Sisters

Born Died

Spouse

Born Died

Spouse

Born Died

Spouse

Born Died

Spouse

Born Died

Spouse

Wife's Grandfather's Nephews & Nieces

Born	*Died*	*Spouse*
Born	*Died*	*Spouse*
Born	*Died*	*Spouse*
Born	*Died*	*Spouse*
Born	*Died*	*Spouse*

Born	*Died*	*Spouse*
Born	*Died*	*Spouse*
Born	*Died*	*Spouse*
Born	*Died*	*Spouse*
Born	*Died*	*Spouse*

Born	*Died*	*Spouse*
Born	*Died*	*Spouse*
Born	*Died*	*Spouse*
Born	*Died*	*Spouse*
Born	*Died*	*Spouse*

Born	*Died*	*Spouse*
Born	*Died*	*Spouse*
Born	*Died*	*Spouse*
Born	*Died*	*Spouse*
Born	*Died*	*Spouse*

Born	*Died*	*Spouse*
Born	*Died*	*Spouse*
Born	*Died*	*Spouse*
Born	*Died*	*Spouse*
Born	*Died*	*Spouse*

Wife's Maternal Grandparents

Grandmother

Wife's Grandmother's Brothers & Sisters

Born Died

Spouse

Born Died

Spouse

Born Died

Spouse

Born Died

Spouse

Born Died

Spouse

Wife's Grandmother's Nephews & Nieces

Born	Died	Spouse
Born	Died	Spouse
Born	Died	Spouse
Born	Died	Spouse
Born	Died	Spouse

Born	Died	Spouse
Born	Died	Spouse
Born	Died	Spouse
Born	Died	Spouse
Born	Died	Spouse

Born	Died	Spouse
Born	Died	Spouse
Born	Died	Spouse
Born	Died	Spouse
Born	Died	Spouse

Born	Died	Spouse
Born	Died	Spouse
Born	Died	Spouse
Born	Died	Spouse
Born	Died	Spouse

Born	Died	Spouse
Born	Died	Spouse
Born	Died	Spouse
Born	Died	Spouse
Born	Died	Spouse

Wife's Great Grandparents

Wife's Great Grandparents

Weddings

Bride ....

Groom ....

Date ....

Bridesmaids/Matron of Honour

....

....

....

Best Man ....

Church ....

....

....

Reception ....

....

Notes ....

....

"There is no more lovely, friendly and charming relationship, communion or company than a good marriage."
MARTIN LUTHER

Bride ....
Groom ....
Date ....

Bridesmaids/Matron of Honour

....
....
....

Best Man ....

Church ....
....
....

Reception ....
....

Notes ....
....

Weddings

continued

Bride ....

Groom ....

Date ....

Bridesmaids/Matron of Honour

....

....

....

Best Man ....

Church ....

....

....

Reception ....

....

Notes ....

....

Weddings

Bride ....
Groom ....

Date ....

Bridesmaids/Matron of Honour

....

....

....

Best Man ....

Church ....

....

....

Reception ....

....

Notes ....

....

Weddings

continued

Bride ....

Groom ....

Date ....

Bridesmaids/Matron of Honour

....

....

....

Best Man ....

Church ....

....

....

Reception ....

....

Notes ....

....

Weddings

Bride ....

Groom ....

Date ....

Bridesmaids/Matron of Honour

....

....

....

Best Man ....

Church ....

....

....

Reception ....

....

Notes ....

....

Weddings

continued

Bride ....

Groom ....

Date ....

Bridesmaids/Matron of Honour

....

....

....

Best Man ....

Church ....

....

....

Reception ....

....

Notes ....

....

Weddings

Bride ....

Groom ....

Date ....

Bridesmaids/Matron of Honour

....

....

....

Best Man ....

Church ....

....

....

Reception ....

....

Notes ....

....

Weddings

continued

Bride ....

Groom ....

Date ....

Bridesmaids/Matron of Honour

....

....

....

Best Man ....

Church ....

....

....

Reception ....

....

Notes ....

....

Weddings

Bride ....

Groom ....

Date ....

Bridesmaids/Matron of Honour

....

....

....

Best Man ....

Church ....

....

....

Reception ....

....

Notes ....

....

Photographs & Memories

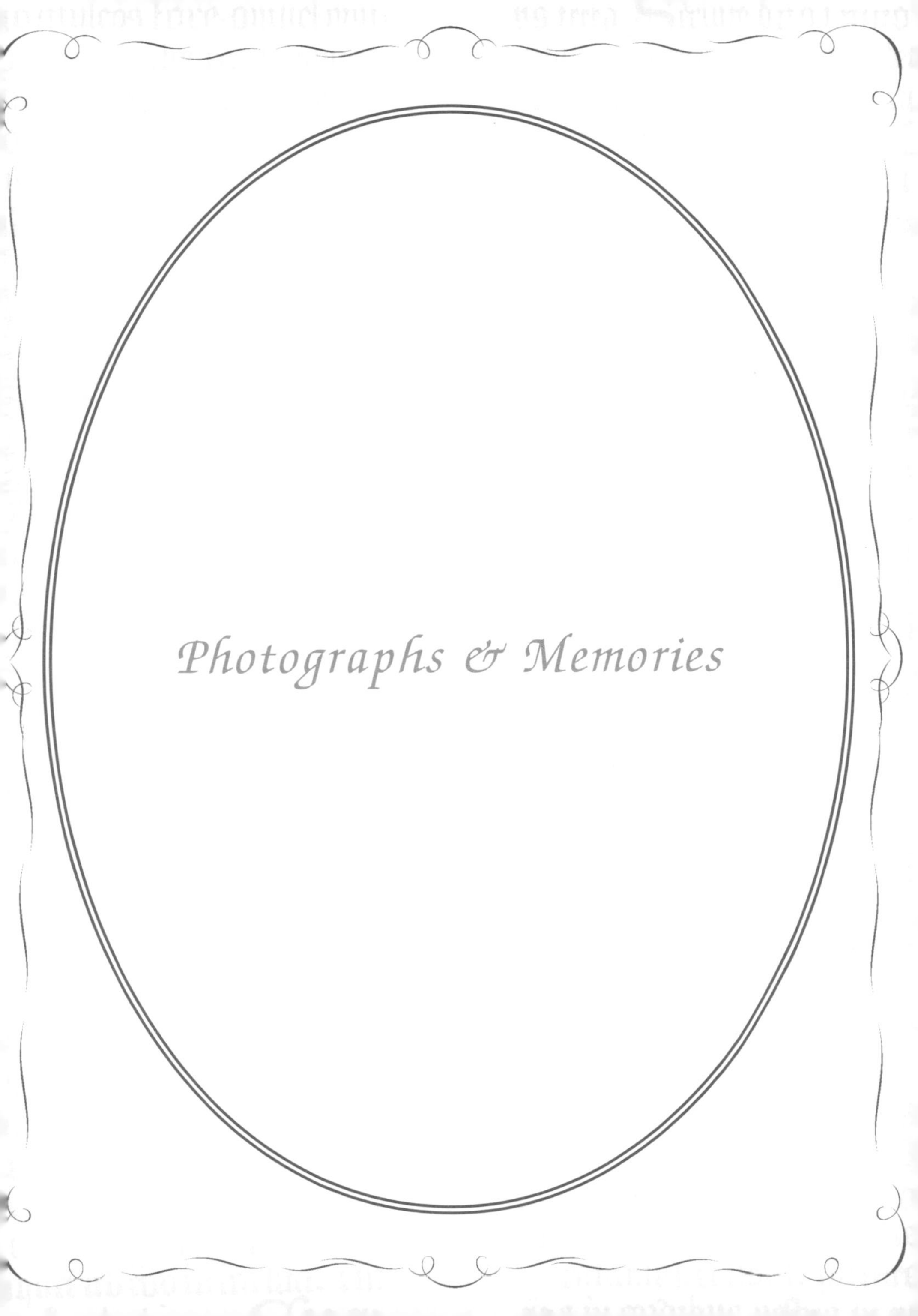
Photographs & Memories

Photographs & Memories

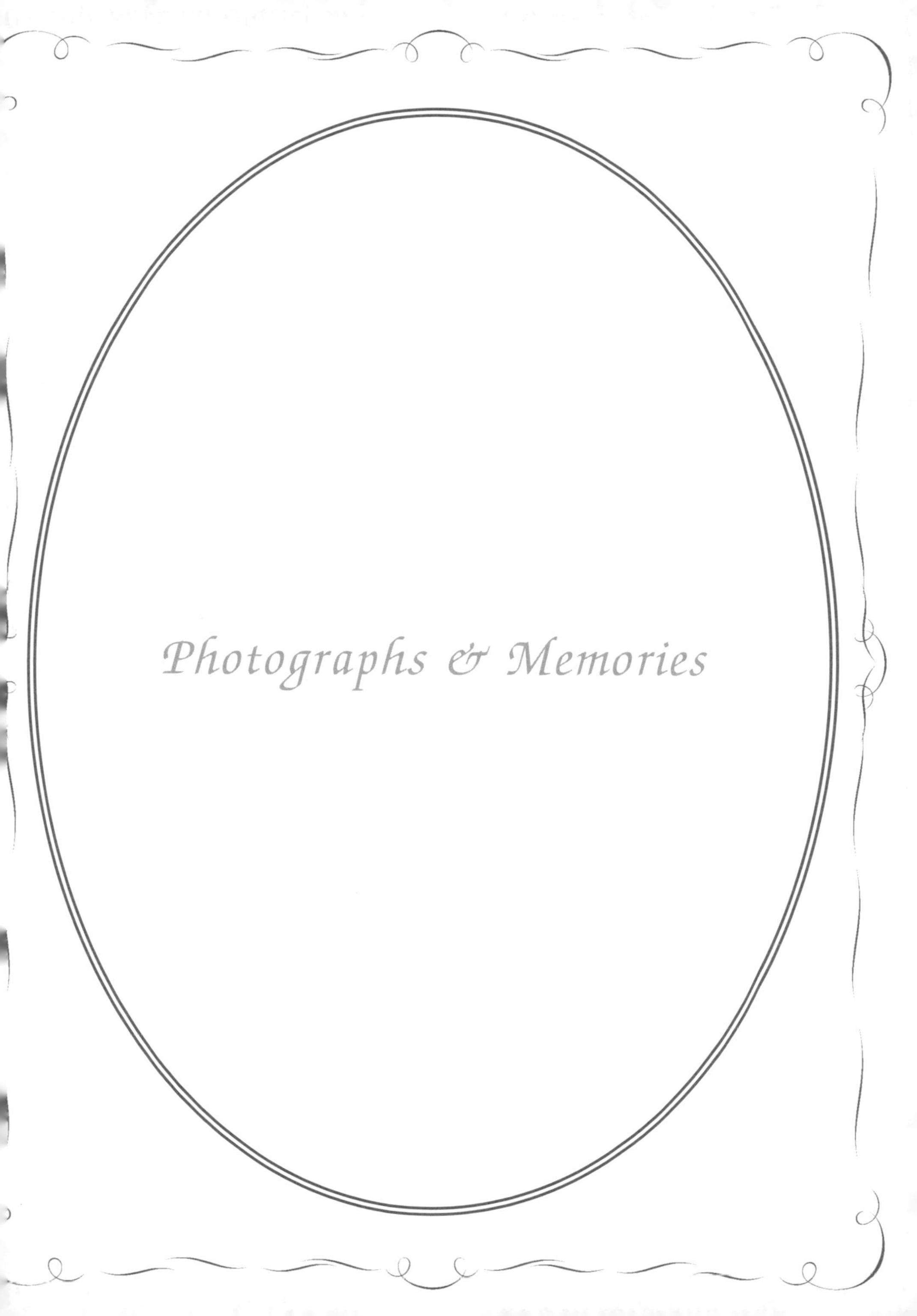
Photographs & Memories

Photographs & Memories

Weddings

continued

Bride ....

Groom ....

Date ....

Bridesmaids/Matron of Honour

....

....

....

Best Man ....

Church ....

....

....

Reception ....

....

Notes ....

....

Weddings

continued

Bride ....

Groom ....

Date ....

Bridesmaids/Matron of Honour

....

....

....

Best Man ....

Church ....

....

....

Reception ....

....

Notes ....

....

Weddings

Bride ....

Groom ....

Date ....

Bridesmaids/Matron of Honour

....

....

....

Best Man ....

Church ....

....

....

Reception ....

....

Notes ....

....

Weddings

continued

Bride ....

Groom ....

Date ....

Bridesmaids/Matron of Honour

....

....

....

Best Man ....

Church ....

....

....

Reception ....

....

Notes ....

....

Weddings

Bride ....

Groom ....

Date ....

Bridesmaids/Matron of Honour

....

....

....

Best Man ....

Church ....

....

....

Reception ....

....

Notes ....

....

Photographs & Memories

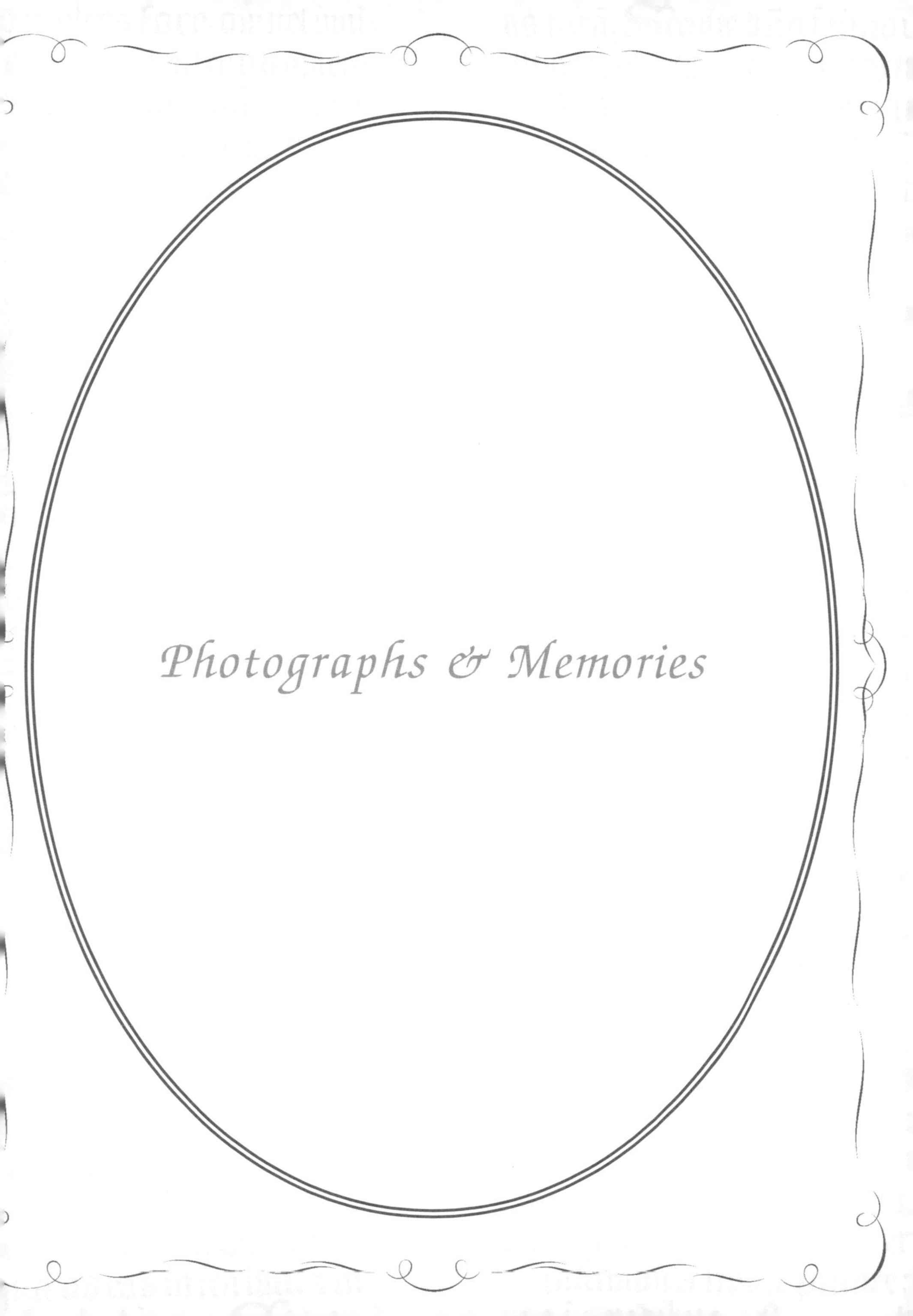
Photographs & Memories

Weddings

continued

Bride ....

Groom ....

Date ....

Bridesmaids/Matron of Honour

....

....

....

Best Man ....

Church ....

....

....

Reception ....

....

Notes ....

....

Weddings

Bride ....

Groom ....

Date ....

Bridesmaids/Matron of Honour

....

....

....

Best Man ....

Church ....

....

....

Reception ....

....

Notes ....

....

Family Notes

Family Notes

Family Notes

Family Notes

Religious Ceremonies

Name ....

Ceremony or Occasion ....

....

Date ....

Godparents or Sponsors ....

Place ....

....

Notes ....

Name ....

Ceremony or Occasion ....

....

Date ....

Godparents or Sponsors ....

Place ....

....

Notes ....

"God gave us memories that we might have roses in December."
JAMES M BARRIE

Name ....
Ceremony or Occasion ....

....

Date ....
Godparents or Sponsors ....
Place ....

....

Notes ....

Name ....
Ceremony or Occasion ....

....

Date ....
Godparents or Sponsors ....
Place ....

....

Notes ....

Religious Ceremonies

continued

Name ....

Ceremony or Occasion ....

....

Date ....

Godparents or Sponsors ....

Place ....

....

Notes ....

Name ....

Ceremony or Occasion ....

....

Date ....

Godparents or Sponsors ....

Place ....

....

Notes ....

Name ....

Ceremony or Occasion ....

....

Date ....

Godparents or Sponsors ....

Place ....

....

Notes ....

Name ....

Ceremony or Occasion ....

....

Date ....

Godparents or Sponsors ....

Place ....

....

Notes ....

Religious Ceremonies

continued

Name ....

Ceremony or Occasion ....

....

Date ....

Godparents or Sponsors ....

Place ....

....

Notes ....

Name ....

Ceremony or Occasion ....

....

Date ....

Godparents or Sponsors ....

Place ....

....

Notes ....

Name ....

Ceremony or Occasion ....

....

Date ....

Godparents or Sponsors ....

Place ....

....

Notes ....

Name ....

Ceremony or Occasion ....

....

Date ....

Godparents or Sponsors ....

Place ....

....

Notes ....

Education

Name ....

Educational Establishment

....

Dates ....

Qualification ....

Notes ....

....

....

Name ....

Educational Establishment

....

Dates ....

Qualification ....

Notes ....

....

....

"Education is what survives when what has been learnt has been forgotten."
B F SKINNER

Name ....

Educational Establishment

....

Dates ....

Qualification ....

Notes ....

....

....

Name ....

Educational Establishment

....

Dates ....

Qualification ....

Notes ....

....

....

Education

continued

Name ....

Educational Establishment

....

Dates ....

Qualification ....

Notes ....

....

....

Name ....

Educational Establishment

....

Dates ....

Qualification ....

Notes ....

....

....

Name ....

Educational Establishment

....

Dates ....

Qualification ....

Notes ....

....

....

Name ....

Educational Establishment

....

Dates ....

Qualification ....

Notes ....

....

....

Education

continued

Name ....

Educational Establishment

....

Dates ....

Qualification ....

Notes ....

....

....

Name ....

Educational Establishment

....

Dates ....

Qualification ....

Notes ....

....

....

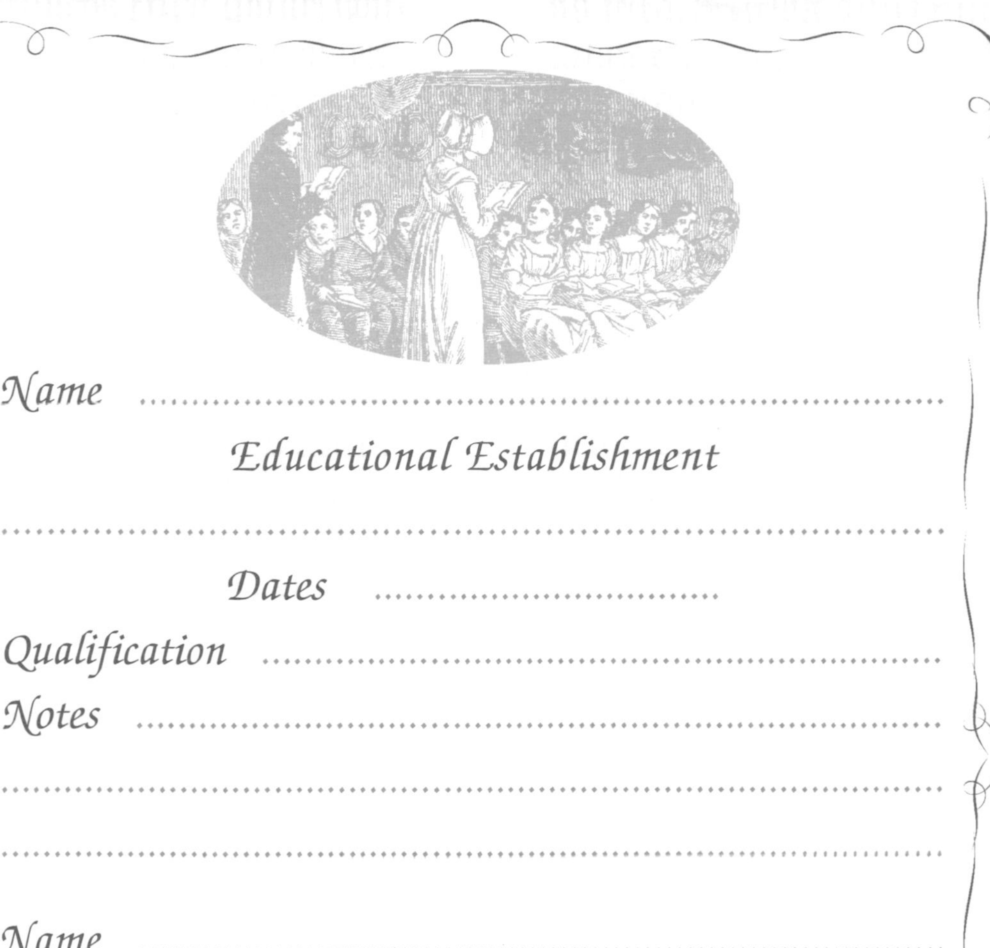

Name ....

Educational Establishment

....

Dates ....

Qualification ....

Notes ....

....

....

Name ....

Educational Establishment

....

Dates ....

Qualification ....

Notes ....

....

....

Education

Special Achievements

Name ....

Educational Establishment

....

Dates ....

Qualification ....

Notes ....

....

....

Name ....

Educational Establishment

....

Dates ....

Qualification ....

Notes ....

....

....

Name ....

Educational Establishment

....

Dates ....

Qualification ....

Notes ....

....

....

Name ....

Educational Establishment

....

Dates ....

Qualification ....

Notes ....

....

....

Education
Special Achievements

continued

Name ....

Educational Establishment

....

Dates ....

Qualification ....

Notes ....

....

....

Name ....

Educational Establishment

....

Dates ....

Qualification ....

Notes ....

....

....

Name ....

Educational Establishment

....

Dates ....

Qualification ....

Notes ....

....

....

Name ....

Educational Establishment

....

Dates ....

Qualification ....

Notes ....

....

....

Education
Special Achievements

continued

Name ....

Educational Establishment

....

Dates ....

Qualification ....

Notes ....

....

....

Name ....

Educational Establishment

....

Dates ....

Qualification ....

Notes ....

....

....

Name ....

Educational Establishment

....

Dates ....

Qualification ....

Notes ....

....

....

Name ....

Educational Establishment

....

Dates ....

Qualification ....

Notes ....

....

....

Business

Name ....
Business ....
....
Dates ....
Notes ....
....
....
....

Name ....
Business ....
....
Dates ....
Notes ....
....
....
....

"Whenever you see a successful business, someone once made a courageous decision."
PETER DRUCKER

Name ....
Business ....

....

Dates ....
Notes ....

....

....

....

Name ....
Business ....

....

Dates ....
Notes ....

....

....

....

Business

continued

Name ....

Business ....

....

Dates ....

Notes ....

....

....

....

Name ....

Business ....

....

Dates ....

Notes ....

....

....

....

Name ....

Business ....

....

Dates ....

Notes ....

....

....

....

Name ....

Business ....

....

Dates ....

Notes ....

....

....

....

Business

continued

Name ....

Business ....

....

Dates ....

Notes ....

....

....

....

Name ....

Business ....

....

Dates ....

Notes ....

....

....

....

Name ....

Business ....

....

Dates ....

Notes ....

....

....

....

Name ....

Business ....

....

Dates ....

Notes ....

....

....

....

Family homes

Name of House ....

Address ....

....

....

Dates (from) .... to ....

Purchase Value ....

Sale Value ....

Notes ....

....

Name of House ....

Address ....

....

....

Dates (from) .... to ....

Purchase Value ....

Sale Value ....

Notes ....

....

"The home of everyone is to him his castle and fortress, as well for his defence against injury and violence, as for his repose."
EDWARD COKE"

Name of House ....
Address ....
....
....
Dates (from) .... to ....
Purchase Value ....
Sale Value ....
Notes ....
....

Name of House ....
Address ....
....
....
Dates (from) .... to ....
Purchase Value ....
Sale Value ....
Notes ....
....

Family homes

continued

Name of House ....

Address ....

....

....

Dates (from) .... to ....

Purchase Value ....

Sale Value ....

Notes ....

....

Name of House ....

Address ....

....

....

Dates (from) .... to ....

Purchase Value ....

Sale Value ....

Notes ....

....

Name of House ....
Address ....

....

....

Dates (from) .... *to* ....
Purchase Value ....
Sale Value ....
Notes ....

....

Name of House ....
Address ....

....

....

Dates (from) .... *to* ....
Purchase Value ....
Sale Value ....
Notes ....

....

Family homes

continued

Name of House ....

Address ....

....

....

Dates (from) .... to ....

Purchase Value ....

Sale Value ....

Notes ....

....

Name of House ....

Address ....

....

....

Dates (from) .... to ....

Purchase Value ....

Sale Value ....

Notes ....

....

Name of House ....

Address ....

....

....

Dates (from) .... *to* ....

Purchase Value ....

Sale Value ....

Notes ....

....

Name of House ....

Address ....

....

....

Dates (from) .... *to* ....

Purchase Value ....

Sale Value ....

Notes ....

....

Family homes

continued

Name of House ....
Address ....
....
....
Dates (from) .... *to* ....
Purchase Value ....
Sale Value ....
Notes ....
....

Name of House ....
Address ....
....
....
Dates (from) .... *to* ....
Purchase Value ....
Sale Value ....
Notes ....
....

Name of House ....
Address ....

....

....

Dates (from) .... *to* ....
Purchase Value ....
Sale Value ....
Notes ....

....

Name of House ....
Address ....

....

....

Dates (from) .... *to* ....
Purchase Value ....
Sale Value ....
Notes ....

....

Family Vehicles

Owner ....

Model ....

Colour .... Year ....

Dates of Ownership ....

Notes ....

....

Owner ....

Model ....

Colour .... Year ....

Dates of Ownership ....

Notes ....

....

Owner ....

Model ....

Colour .... Year ....

Dates of Ownership ....

Notes ....

....

Owner ....

Model ....

Colour .... *Year* ....

Dates of Ownership ....

Notes ....

....

Owner ....

Model ....

Colour .... *Year* ....

Dates of Ownership ....

Notes ....

....

Owner ....

Model ....

Colour .... *Year* ....

Dates of Ownership ....

Notes ....

....

Family Vehicles

Owner ....
Model ....
Colour .... Year ....
Dates of Ownership ....
Notes ....
....

Owner ....
Model ....
Colour .... Year ....
Dates of Ownership ....
Notes ....
....

Owner ....
Model ....
Colour .... Year ....
Dates of Ownership ....
Notes ....
....

Family Notes

Family Pets

Pet's Name ....

Type of Animal ....

Dates of Ownership ....

Notes ....

....

Pet's Name ....

Type of Animal ....

Dates of Ownership ....

Notes ....

....

Pet's Name ....

Type of Animal ....

Dates of Ownership ....

Notes ....

....

Animals are such agreeable friends – they ask no questions, they pass no criticisms."

GEORGE ELIOT

Pet's Name ....

Type of Animal ....

Dates of Ownership ....

Notes ....

....

Pet's Name ....

Type of Animal ....

Dates of Ownership ....

Notes ....

....

Pet's Name ....

Type of Animal ....

Dates of Ownership ....

Notes ....

....

Family Pets

continued

Pet's Name ....

Type of Animal ....

Dates of Ownership ....

Notes ....

....

Pet's Name ....

Type of Animal ....

Dates of Ownership ....

Notes ....

....

Pet's Name ....

Type of Animal ....

Dates of Ownership ....

Notes ....

....

Pet's Name ....

Type of Animal ....

Dates of Ownership ....

Notes ....

....

Pet's Name ....

Type of Animal ....

Dates of Ownership ....

Notes ....

....

Pet's Name ....

Type of Animal ....

Dates of Ownership ....

Notes ....

....

Events to remember

Event ....

Date ....

Notes ....

....

....

....

Event ....

Date ....

Notes ....

....

....

....

Event ....

Date ....

Notes ....

....

....

....

Event ....
Date ....
Notes ....

....

....

....

Event ....
Date ....
Notes ....

....

....

....

Event ....
Date ....
Notes ....

....

....

....

Events to remember

continued

Event ....

Date ....

Notes ....

....

....

....

Event ....

Date ....

Notes ....

....

....

....

Event ....

Date ....

Notes ....

....

....

....

Event ....

Date ....

Notes ....

....

....

....

Event ....

Date ....

Notes ....

....

....

....

Event ....

Date ....

Notes ....

....

....

....

Events to remember

continued

Event ....

Date ....

Notes ....

....

....

....

Event ....

Date ....

Notes ....

....

....

....

Event ....

Date ....

Notes ....

....

....

....

Event
Date
Notes

Event
Date
Notes

Event
Date
Notes

Reunions

Occasion ....

Date ....

Location ....

Who Attended ....

....

....

Notes ....

....

....

Occasion ....

Date ....

Location ....

Who Attended ....

....

....

Notes ....

....

....

"A friend is a gift you give yourself."

Robert Louis Stevenson

Occasion ....

Date ....

Location ....

Who Attended ....

....

....

Notes ....

....

....

Occasion ....

Date ....

Location ....

Who Attended ....

....

....

Notes ....

....

....

Reunions

continued

Occasion ....

Date ....

Location ....

Who Attended ....

....

....

Notes ....

....

....

Occasion ....

Date ....

Location ....

Who Attended ....

....

....

Notes ....

....

....

Occasion ....

Date ....

Location ....

Who Attended ....

....

....

Notes ....

....

....

Occasion ....

Date ....

Location ....

Who Attended ....

....

....

Notes ....

....

....

Reunions

continued

Occasion ....

Date ....

Location ....

Who Attended ....

....

....

Notes ....

....

....

Occasion ....

Date ....

Location ....

Who Attended ....

....

....

Notes ....

....

....

Occasion ....

Date ....

Location ....

Who Attended ....

....

....

Notes ....

....

....

Occasion ....

Date ....

Location ....

Who Attended ....

....

....

Notes ....

....

....

Family holidays

Where ....

Dates ....

Location ....

Who was there ....

....

Notes ....

....

....

....

Where ....

Dates ....

Location ....

Who was there ....

....

Notes ....

....

....

....

"What is this life if, full of care,
We have no time to s
stand and stare?"
W H Davies

Where ....

Dates ....

Location ....

Who was there ....

....

Notes ....

....

....

....

Where ....

Dates ....

Location ....

Who was there ....

....

Notes ....

....

....

....

Family holidays

continued

Where ....

Dates ....

Location ....

Who was there ....

....

Notes ....

....

....

....

Where ....

Dates ....

Location ....

Who was there ....

....

Notes ....

....

....

....

Where ....

Dates ....

Location ....

Who was there ....

....

Notes ....

....

....

....

Where ....

Dates ....

Location ....

Who was there ....

....

Notes ....

....

....

....

Family holidays

continued

Where ....

Dates ....

Location ....

Who was there ....

....

Notes ....

....

....

....

Where ....

Dates ....

Location ....

Who was there ....

....

Notes ....

....

....

....

Where ....

Dates ....

Location ....

Who was there ....

....

Notes ....

....

....

....

Where ....

Dates ....

Location ....

Who was there ....

....

Notes ....

....

....

....

Family holidays

continued

Where ....

Dates ....

Location ....

Who was there ....

....

Notes ....

....

....

....

Where ....

Dates ....

Location ....

Who was there ....

....

Notes ....

....

....

....

Where ....

Dates ....

Location ....

Who was there ....

....

Notes ....

....

....

....

Where ....

Dates ....

Location ....

Who was there ....

....

Notes ....

....

....

....

Family holidays

continued

Where ....

Dates ....

Location ....

Who was there ....

....

Notes ....

....

....

....

Where ....

Dates ....

Location ....

Who was there ....

....

Notes ....

....

....

....

Where ....

Dates ....

Location ....

Who was there ....

....

Notes ....

....

....

....

Where ....

Dates ....

Location ....

Who was there ....

....

Notes ....

....

....

....

Family holidays

continued

Where ....

Dates ....

Location ....

Who was there ....

....

Notes ....

....

....

....

Where ....

Dates ....

Location ....

Who was there ....

....

Notes ....

....

....

....

Where ....

Dates ....

Location ....

Who was there ....

....

Notes ....

....

....

....

Where ....

Dates ....

Location ....

Who was there ....

....

Notes ....

....

....

....

Photographs & Memories

Photographs & Memories

Illnesses

Name ....
Illness ....
Notes ....
....
....
....

Name ....
Illness ....
Notes ....
....
....
....

Name ....
Illness ....
Notes ....
....
....
....

"I enjoy convalescence. It is the part that makes the illness worth while."

GEORGE BERNARD SHAW

Name ....

Illness ....

Notes ....

....

....

....

Name ....

Illness ....

Notes ....

....

....

....

Name ....

Illness ....

Notes ....

....

....

....

Illnesses

continued

Name ....
Illness ....
Notes ....
....
....
....

Name ....
Illness ....
Notes ....
....
....
....

Name ....
Illness ....
Notes ....
....
....
....

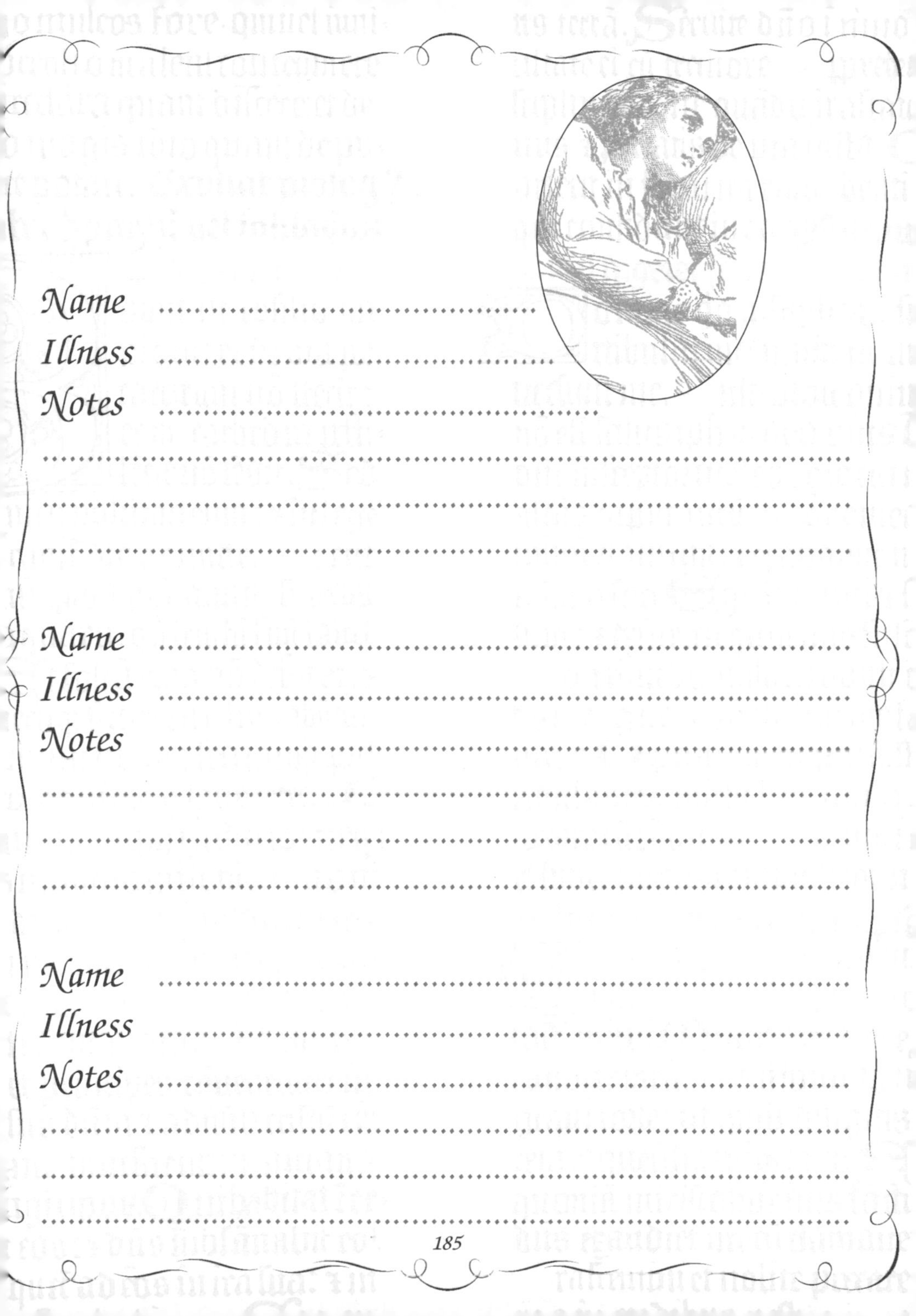

Name ....
Illness ....
Notes ....
....
....
....

Name ....
Illness ....
Notes ....
....
....
....

Name ....
Illness ....
Notes ....
....
....
....

Clubs & Organisations

Name ....
Club/Organisation ....
Notes ....
....
....
....

Name ....
Club/Organisation ....
Notes ....
....
....
....

Name ....
Club/Organisation ....
Notes ....
....
....
....

"I do not care to belong to a club that accepts people like me as members."
GROUCHO MARX

Name ....

Club/Organisation ....

Notes ....

....

....

....

Name ....

Club/Organisation ....

Notes ....

....

....

....

Name ....

Club/Organisation ....

Notes ....

....

....

....

Clubs & Organisations

continued

Name ....

Club/Organisation ....

Notes ....

....

....

....

Name ....

Club/Organisation ....

Notes ....

....

....

....

Name ....

Club/Organisation ....

Notes ....

....

....

....

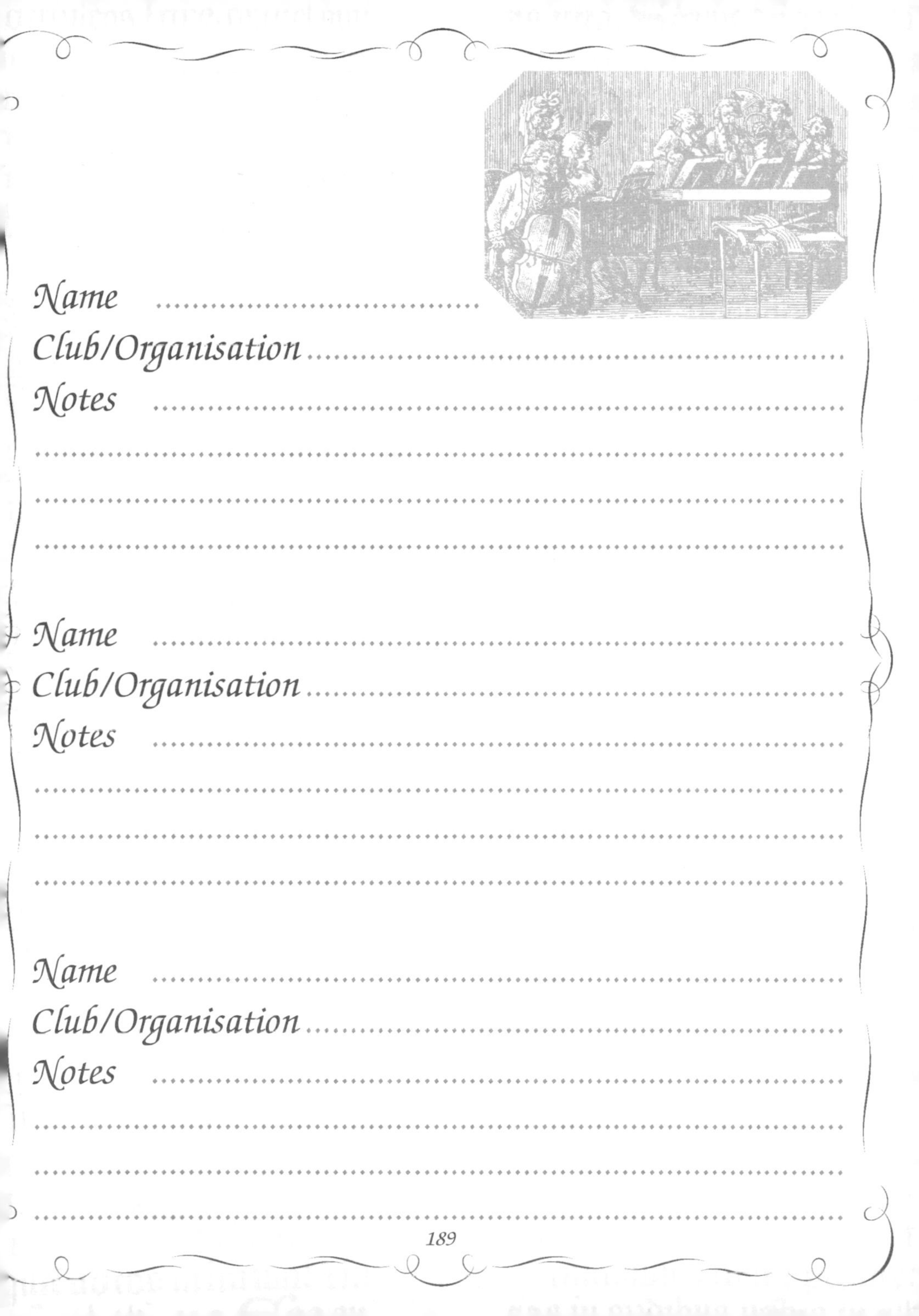

Name ....

Club/Organisation ....

Notes ....

....

....

....

Name ....

Club/Organisation ....

Notes ....

....

....

....

Name ....

Club/Organisation ....

Notes ....

....

....

....

Family Friends

Name ....

Address ....

....

....

Notes ....

....

Name ....

Address ....

....

....

Notes ....

....

Name ....

Address ....

....

....

Notes ....

....

"The ornament of a house is the friends who frequent it."
EMERSON

Name ....
Address ....
....
....
Notes ....
....

Name ....
Address ....
....
....
Notes ....
....

Name ....
Address ....
....
....
Notes ....
....

Family Friends

continued

Name ....
Address ....
....
....
Notes ....
....

Name ....
Address ....
....
....
Notes ....
....

Name ....
Address ....
....
....
Notes ....
....

Name
Address

Notes

Name
Address

Notes

Name
Address

Notes

Family Friends

continued

Name ....
Address ....
....
....
Notes ....
....

Name ....
Address ....
....
....
Notes ....
....

Name ....
Address ....
....
....
Notes ....
....

Name ....
Address ....
....
....
Notes ....
....

Name ....
Address ....
....
....
Notes ....
....

Name ....
Address ....
....
....
Notes ....
....

Family Friends

continued

Name ....

Address ....

....

....

Notes ....

....

Name ....

Address ....

....

....

Notes ....

....

Name ....

Address ....

....

....

Notes ....

....

Name

Address

Notes

Name

Address

Notes

Name

Address

Notes

Family Friends

continued

Name ....

Address ....

....

....

Notes ....

....

Name ....

Address ....

....

....

Notes ....

....

Name ....

Address ....

....

....

Notes ....

....

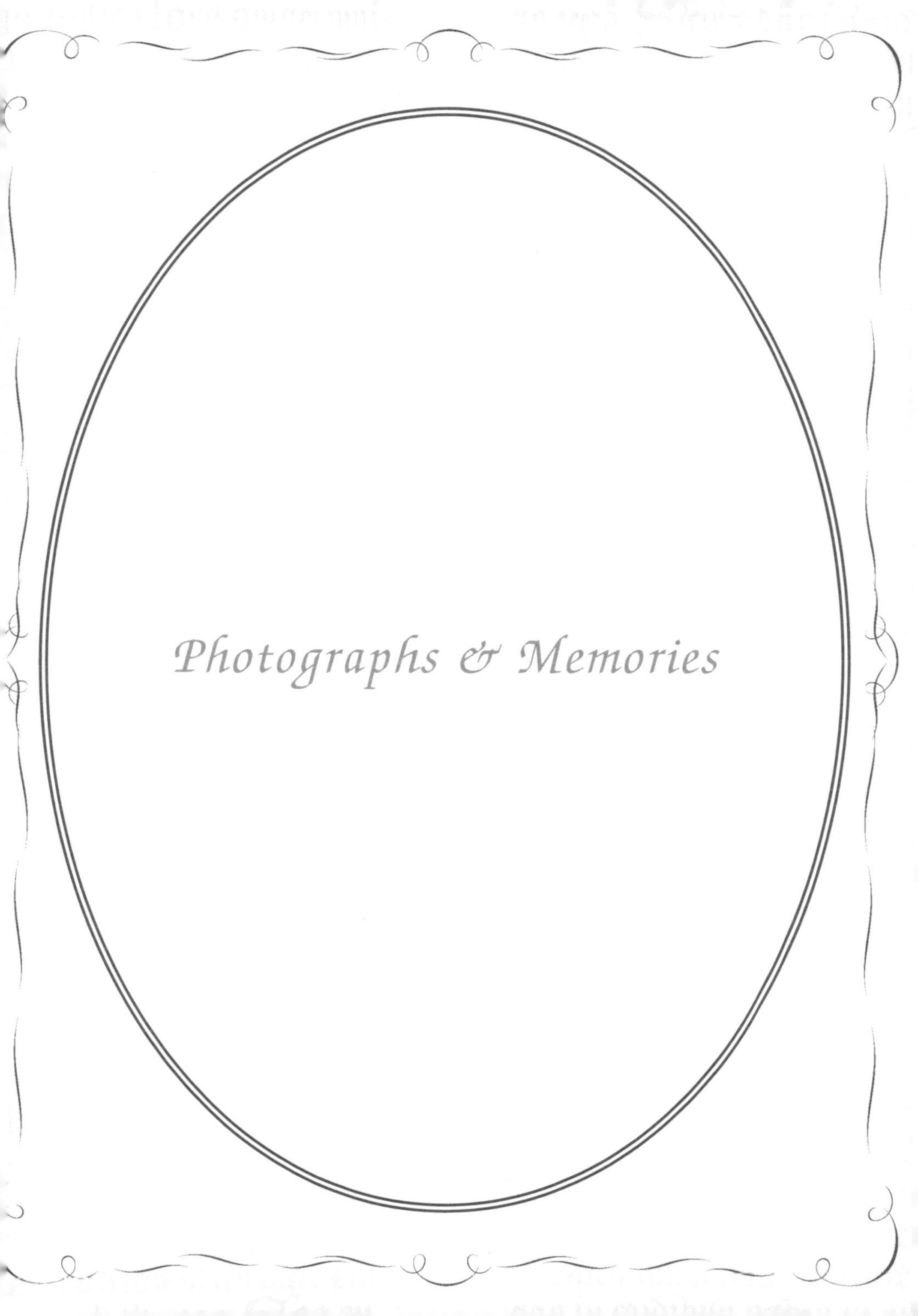
Photographs & Memories

Friends Notes

Friends Notes

Friends Notes

Friends Notes

Family Hobbies

Name ....

Hobby ....

....

Notes ....

....

....

Name ....

Hobby ....

....

Notes ....

....

....

Name ....

....

Hobby ....

....

Notes ....

....

....

"To the art of working well a civilized race would add the art of playing well."
GEORGE SANTAYANA

Name ....
Hobby ....

....

Notes ....

....

....

Name ....
Hobby ....

....

Notes ....

....

....

Name ....

....

Hobby ....

....

Notes ....

....

....

Family Hobbies

continued

Name ....
Hobby ....

....

Notes ....

....

....

Name ....
Hobby ....

....

Notes ....

....

....

Name ....

....

Hobby ....

....

Notes ....

....

....

Name ....

Hobby ....

....

Notes ....

....

....

Name ....

Hobby ....

....

Notes ....

....

....

Name ....

....

Hobby ....

....

Notes ....

....

....

Family Sports

Name ....
Sport ....
....
Notes ....
....
....

Name ....
Sport ....
....
Notes ....
....
....

Name ....
....
Sport ....
....
Notes ....
....
....

"Sports do not build character.
They reveal it."
HEYWOOD BROUN

Name ....
Sport ....

....

Notes ....

....

....

Name ....
Sport ....

....

Notes ....

....

....

Name ....

....

Sport ....

....

Notes ....

....

....

Family Sports

continued

Name ....

Sport ....

....

Notes ....

....

....

Name ....

Sport ....

....

Notes ....

....

....

Name ....

....

Sport ....

....

Notes ....

....

....

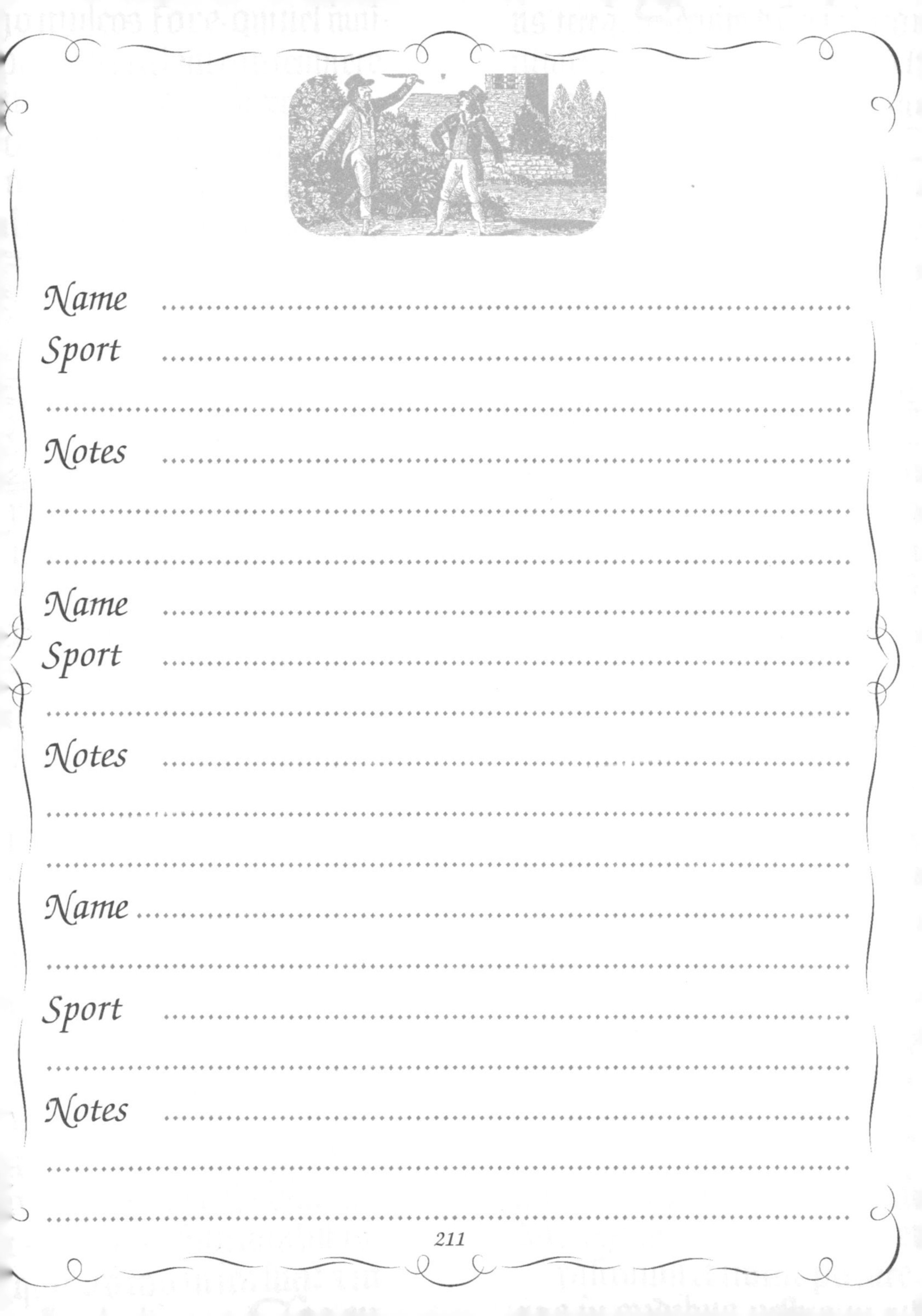

Name ....
Sport ....

....

Notes ....

....

....

Name ....
Sport ....

....

Notes ....

....

....

Name ....

....

Sport ....

....

Notes ....

....

....

Family Collections & Heirlooms

Name ....

Item ....

Notes ....

....

....

Name ....

Item ....

Notes ....

....

....

Name ....

....

Item ....

Notes ....

....

....

"Bliss in possession will not last;
Remembered joys are never past."
James Montgomery

Name ....

Item ....

Notes ....

....

....

Name ....

Item ....

Notes ....

....

....

Name ....

....

Item ....

Notes ....

....

....

Family Collections & Heirlooms

continued

Name ....

Item ....

Notes ....

....

....

Name ....

Item ....

Notes ....

....

....

Name ....

....

Item ....

Notes ....

....

....

Name ....

Item ....

Notes ....

....

....

Name ....

Item ....

Notes ....

....

....

Name ....

....

Item ....

Notes ....

....

....

Family Collections & Heirlooms

continued

Name ....

Item ....

Notes ....

....

....

Name ....

Item ....

Notes ....

....

....

Name ....

....

Item ....

Notes ....

....

....

Name ....

Item ....

Notes ....

....

....

Name ....

Item ....

Notes ....

....

....

Name ....

....

Item ....

Notes ....

....

....

Family Notes

Family Notes

Family Notes

Family Notes

Photographs & Memories

Photographs & Memories

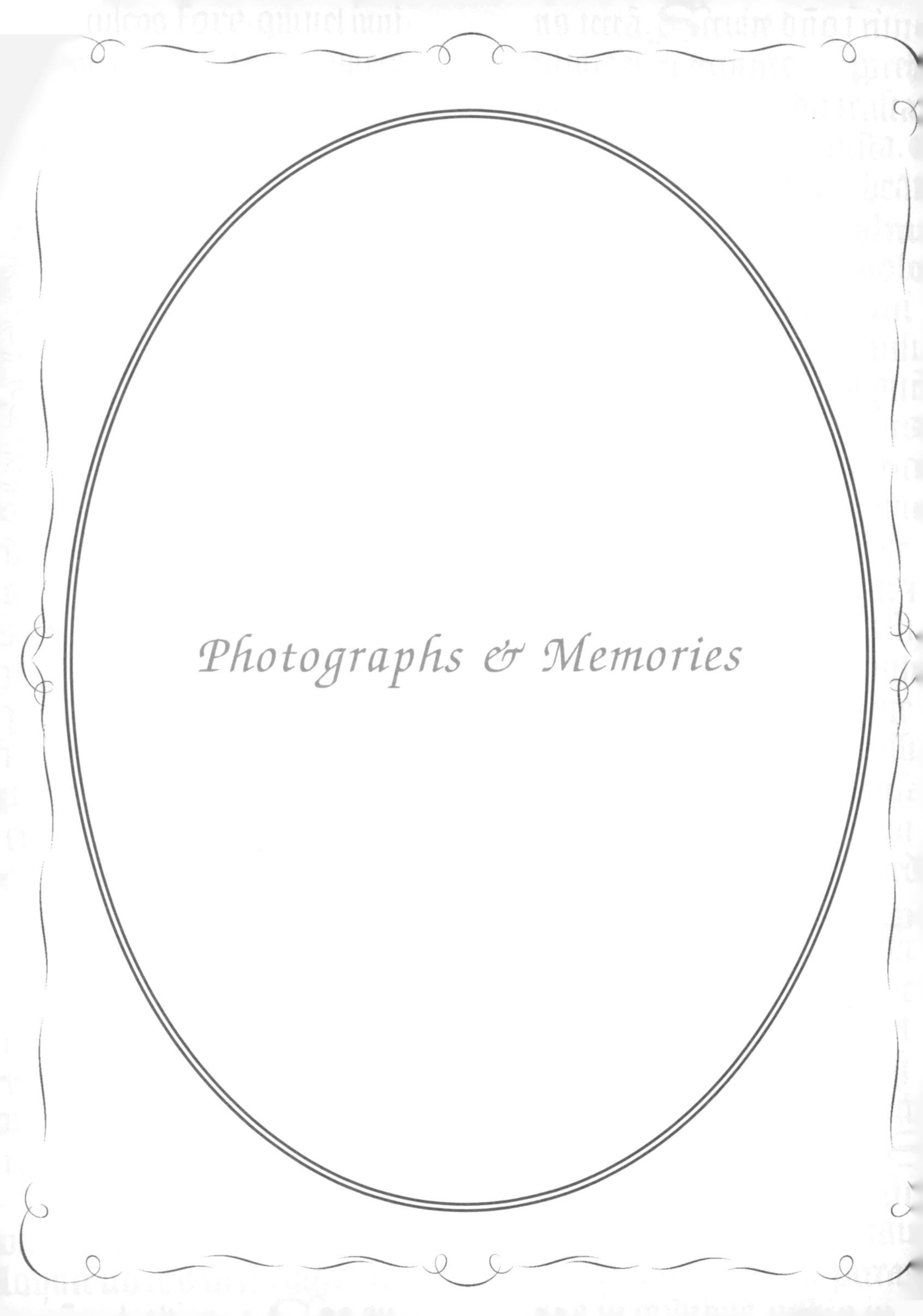
Photographs & Memories

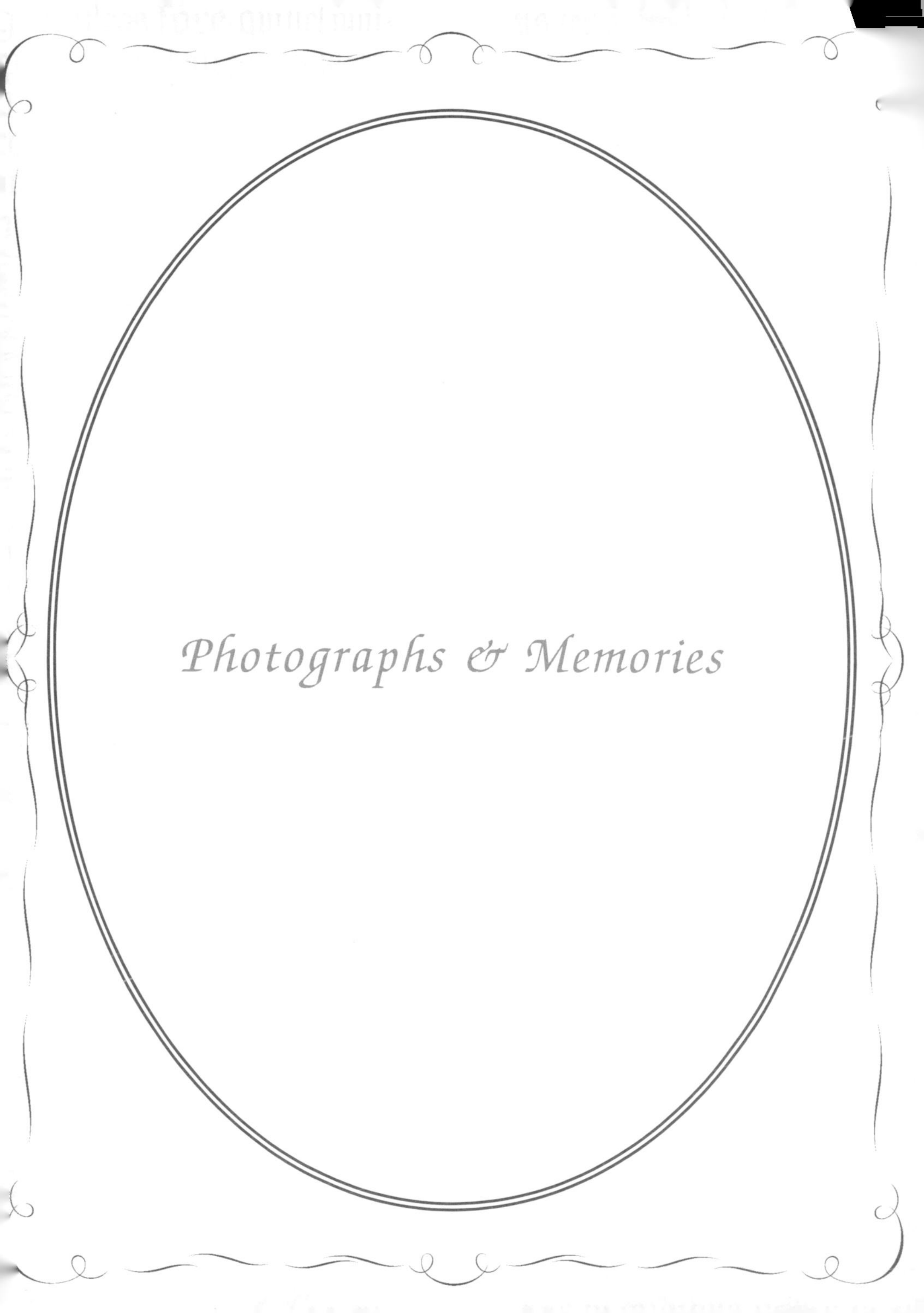
Photographs & Memories

Family Notes

Family Notes

Family Bereavements

Family Bereavements

Family Bereavements

Family Bereavements

Family Bereavements

Family Bereavements